Find the three differences between the two pictures and circle them.

one! ✓

Trace over the ripples the sharks have made in the water.

Zoom!

Draw lines to match the sharks' bodies to their tails.

Splash
splash!

D d D d   E e E e

Help the diver swim to safety!

Draw in the missing
tail and fins.

Well done!

Ff Ff   Gg Gg

Count the stripy fish and write the number in the box.

Trace over the missing letters to complete the words.

Shark Shark

Chomp chomp!

Hh Hh   Ii Ii

Circle the picture that is the odd one out.

Trace over the missing letters to complete the words.

Shark Shark

Well done!

Jj Jj   Kk Kk

Follow the line around the white-tip reef shark.

Chomp!

Trace around the pattern
on the shark.

Snap snap!

Ll Ll Ll   Mm   Mm

Circle the colours of the shark.

Splash

splash!

Purple
Orange

Blue
Yellow

Black
Green

Grey
White

Draw lines to match the sharks' heads to their bodies.

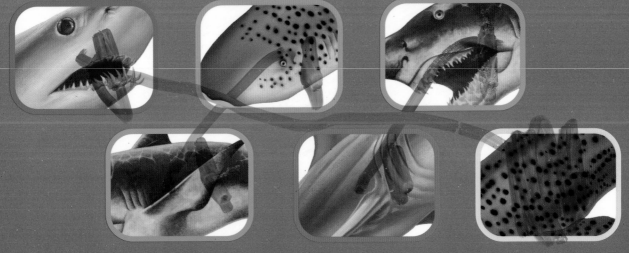

Well done!

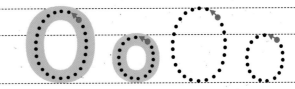

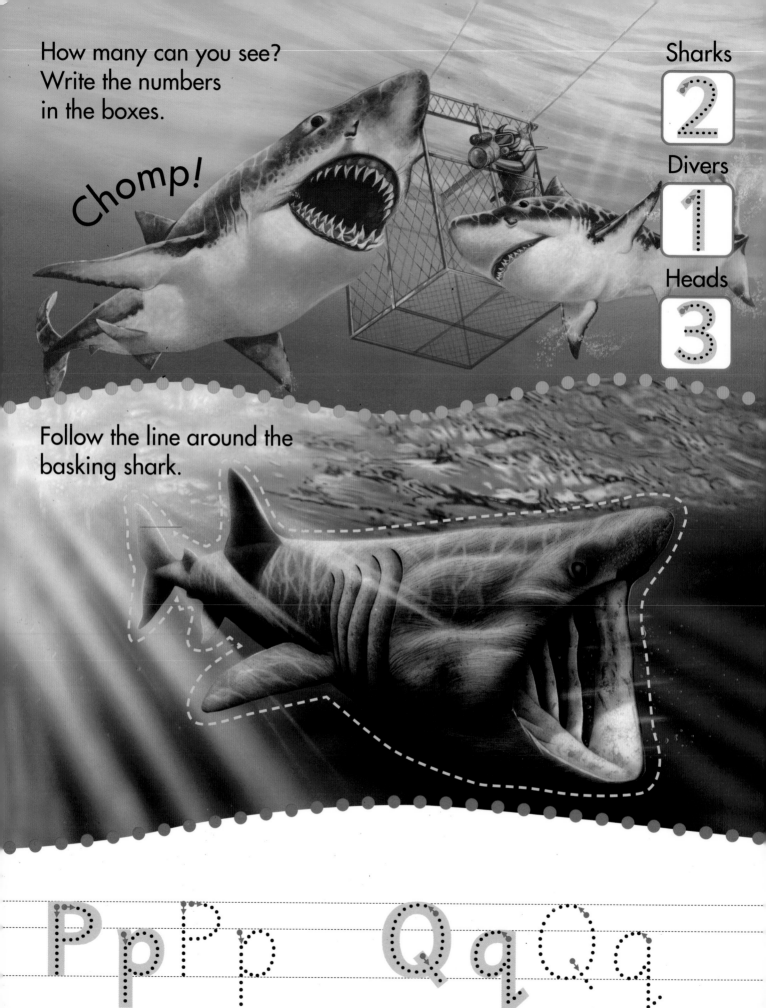

How many can you see?
Write the numbers
in the boxes.

Chomp!

Sharks

2

Divers

1

Heads

3

Follow the line around the
basking shark.

P p P p   Q q Q q

Draw around the outline of the great white shark.

Trace over the missing letters to complete the words.

Shark   Shark

Splash splash!

Well done!

Rr Rr   Ss Ss

Help the shark swim through the fish.

Splash!

Draw in the thresher shark's missing tail.

Tt Tt Uu Uu

Trace the line to draw
the black-tip reef shark.

Circle the noises a shark makes.

MOOOOoo!

Snap
snap!

Chomp
chomp!

Miaow
miaow!

Splash
splash!

Chomp chomp!

Well done!

V v v v   W w w w

Draw over the lines to get to the sharks.

Trace over the numbers and draw around the fish.